I loved the book! It's really so deceptive
the more you read it, the more profoun
changing and goes beyond those books
weaknesses and the ups and downs of da
more importantly, the space to feel that i

Dr Sanda Ionescu, Sociologist & Business Coach

What a remarkable book – original, immediately engaging and funny. One can't help but get taken along by the insight, gentleness and remarkable ability of the author to make a statement that stops you dead in your tracks. It really is a book for everyone and it has a charm all of its own.

Dr Erica Warner, Clinical Psychologist

Her clear and accessible explanation on how to regain a sense of balance and perspective [by] engaging with life, with all its complexities, its sorrows and its joys ... will provide the support that will enable us to 'tread caringly and carefully' through life, balancing strength and flexibility and clearly seeing the links between our actions and their consequences.

**Pip Hardy, Director of Pilgrim Projects and
co-founder of the Patient Voices Programme**

I started reading Life Happens with a series of questions in my head. I hadn't expected that [it] would also provide such an essential guide for self-awareness and professional development for all mental health practitioners. The book is presented in an immediately accessible way. The accompanying CDs give a real voice to the author, but the text also feels like a conversation that engages the reader in a nurturing dialogue.

Ian Noonan, Mental Health Lecturer, Kings College London.

Life Happens is a book that I know I will read many times. Cheryl Rezek combines the depth of knowledge that comes from an experienced clinical psychologist with humour and easy advice. It encourages you to both like yourself and to recognize and deal with issues. It is a journey I can recommend!

Roger Puttick, Marketing CEO

I found this book extremely readable and thought provoking. In our sometimes very busy and need to aim high world, it made reflecting on the past and its effects on the future understandable. It is an easy book to dip in and out of.

Maureen Kirby, Administrator

Life Happens

Life Happens

Waking up to yourself and your life in a mindful way.

A thoughtful and effective approach to life, wellbeing, physical illness or emotional distress and symptoms associated with conditions such as stress, depression, anxiety, chronic pain, arthritis, cancer and addiction.

DR CHERYL A REZEK

DISCLAIMER

This book makes no claim to act as a cure, preventative measure or treatment of any condition, nor does it advocate discontinuation of any intervention or treatment. The information in this book is not intended as a substitute for consultation with healthcare professionals. It is the responsibility of the reader to seek consultation from a qualified professional should there be any physical, emotional or psychological concerns. All involvement, including reading of the material, participation in tasks, practices, exercise, mediation and listening to the audio material on the CDs is undertaken on a voluntary basis and solely at the responsibility of the participant. The content of this book expresses the views of the author and does not make any claim to contradict those expressed by other persons. It addresses a wider population and is not intended as a treatment for any conditions or behaviours that require specialist consultation or intervention.

ISBN 978-0-9566020-0-8

Prepared and printed by

York Publishing Services
64 Hallfield Road
Layerthorpe
York
YO31 7ZQ

Tel: 01904 431213

Website: www.yps-publishing.co.uk

Illustrations by Terry Cooper www.terrycooper.co.uk

Sound engineer Graham Puddifoot

Cover design original artwork done by Jon Hilliar www.marianidesign.co.uk and layout by Clare Brayshaw

About the Author

Dr Cheryl Rezek is a Clinical Psychologist who has worked as a consultant in the field of mental health for many years. She combined clinical and academic work, whilst working for mental health organisations and universities. She has worked with children, families and adults in a variety of settings as a clinician and supervisor, as well as developed treatment programmes and headed services. She has considerable experience in the areas of trauma, depression, addictions and offending. Her academic links have included lecturing, heading a specialist teaching unit, and being an external examiner, amongst other roles. She was also involved with a hospice organisation for many years.

Further information can be found at www.cherylrezek.com

Acknowledgements

There have been many known and unknown individuals whose knowledge, theories and experiences have contributed to this book, in one way or another, for many centuries and in a variety of ways. They include not only the teachers and professionals, but the everyday people who have struggled with life and sought to find some understanding of it.

The original concept of mindfulness began in the east as a Buddhist practice about twenty five centuries ago, and has continued to be an integral part of its teachings. In the 1970's, the practices and teachings were adapted for a western audience as a programme to assist individuals with difficulties such as stress and illness, by the Center for Mindfulness, University of Massachusetts, USA, and later taken up by the Centre for Mindfulness Research and Practice, University of Bangor, UK. The basic concepts and practices of mindfulness presented within this book originated from those programmes. Mindfulness work is practiced in numerous countries worldwide, in varying forms.

The psychological concepts are based on theories of mind and human development that have emerged over the decades, of which there are too many to mention by name. The views and ideas offered in this book are predominantly drawn from my experience of working with families and individuals who have come from such diverse backgrounds and yet expressed many of the same emotions.

My thanks to Erica and Mo for their assistance.

Life happens

We are where we are today because of each and every experience that has existed before this moment.

We bring into this moment a condensed version of all our yesterdays and the expectations of all our tomorrows.

We can shift the focus to now, to this exact moment, in order to choose how to live it.

There are no magic wands

Life changes: it throws things at us and it comes and goes leaving behind the horrors and highlights of our lives.

We cling on and we reject, we admire and we despise, we love and we fear, but no matter what we do life happens to all of us for better and for worse, with all its chaos and mess, and all its joys and amazements. We can resent it or delight in it but we cannot stop it from travelling its course. What we can do is make a choice about how we are going to be as we go through it.

In a nutshell

This is not a quick-fix, you-can-change-your-life-in-5-minutes book. Your life hasn't taken 5 minutes to get to where it is, and it won't take 5 minutes to understand or manage it in a different way. A quick-fix may be quick but it seldom has a lasting effect: if it takes 5 minutes to do, it will take 5 minutes to undo.

The content is based on a combination of working as a clinical psychologist for many years across various fields and an interest in mindfulness. It makes no claim to change you or your life, but rather offers the opportunity for you to understand how you came to be as you are, and to develop a different way of managing life, both when times are difficult and harsh, and in those moments when it feels easier and kinder.

It's about stepping back and making choices in a purposeful and caring way, respecting both the decision and the consequences. Mindfulness is a way of being, and combining it with psychology allows the opportunity to approach living in a more insightful, considered and thoughtful manner. It is about making a choice as to how you wish to live and engage within your own life and the wider experiences of living, whilst openly accepting that you are human and fallible, just as you are meant to be. It focuses on being present in your life and the lives of others.

Developing a practice of mindfulness is an intentional decision, just like any other decision you take.

Making sense of our lives

We all need to make sense of what has often seemed senseless in our lives, and it is hard to make sense of others' experiences if we haven't made sense of our own. If we know about the well of human feelings, the madness and the shame, the joy and the disruptions, it is then that we can be alive within our own lives whether we are feeling pleasure, despair or pain. If we avoid ourselves, or keep covered the truth and depth of what we are really experiencing, then we can only know a part of what is happening.

At times, especially when those experiences include despair or anger, we are happy to believe that pushing it aside is worthwhile: but what of the good times, of those moments to which we are oblivious or only half-experiencing? It is then that we deny ourselves the full pleasure of the moment.

We don't wake up one morning and say, 'Today I think I'll become an addict, have a chronic condition, or become depressed.' Some things happen over a long period of time and for a number of different reasons. Once you begin to understand your past experiences and the feelings that accompanied them, and make the links between those and your current actions and feelings, you can start to track what you do and why you do it. We aren't identical products churned out of a sausage machine, so each of us is a one-off item. Even identical twins aren't identical in every respect.

Knowing

I cannot know why the world spins on a pin
or where the wind will whistle.
I cannot find a teardrop in the ocean
or catch a breath in the palm of my hand.
All I can know is what I do
and all I can feel
is what is in my heart.

A common mistake is believing that because you are an adult you should forget past events or interpret them in an emotionless and logical manner. Our heads may tell us one thing, but it is our emotions and unconscious beliefs, often created at an early age, that drive our present actions. It is only when you can find and understand the pieces of the past and begin to fit them together, like a complicated jigsaw puzzle, that you can gain insight and perspective. This in turn will help you to know aspects of yourself that contribute towards both the destructive and the more positive qualities of your life, and provide the opportunity to make shifts in it.

We never know everything about ourselves and often it takes further experiences as we go through life for us to become aware of other aspects of ourselves. Similarly, we may never know the details of why others act as they do. We are all capable of actions ranging from profoundly altruistic to horrifyingly awful, but we may only act on some of them. This process is discussed in further detail in Section 1 – How Did I Get To Be Like This?

"I ONLY CAME TO GET TIPS ON MAKING OUT WITH JANET AT MY 16TH BIRTHDAY PARTY!"

We cannot turn rocks into rivers or trees into streams: we cannot change the fundamentals of who we are so we cannot be who we are not. However, by developing self-awareness and a practice of mindfulness, you will be able to make a choice about how to live and engage with the world in each moment. If you are honest with yourselves then you can maintain balance within your life.

Mindfulness

Mindfulness is the process of paying attention to yourself – to your feelings, thoughts, actions and choices – all within the context of now.

> The concept of mindfulness is not about changing yourself but rather about experiencing and accepting who you are and whatever you are feeling, at this moment.

Mindfulness is about being fully present: it is about being present in the present, and living within this moment in an alert and aware state for whatever is happening. It is not about stilling the mind or removing all sensations or thoughts from it. Rather, it is about becoming aware of all that is happening within yourself, regardless of what it is, and using your breathing as an anchor in order to accept and manage it.

Many people who experience stress, illness, emotional distress or chronic pain have a tendency to lose the belief that they can shift their lives into a more manageable state. Mindfulness can increase your ability to acknowledge and accept states of emotional and physical distress. It not only helps with the difficult aspects of life, but it can also provide a place of support and stability for all times.

It is not a treatment, with the anticipated expectation of a cure, but a way of being. In other words, it is something that can be incorporated into your life with each moment, over the entire span of your lifetime. It cannot be purchased or injected, but it can be nurtured and cultivated.

Components central to mindfulness are compassion and kindness, most importantly towards yourself. No-one thrives on criticism and censure. They may spur one on to achieve, but being judged and attacked has little true value.

A brief history of mindfulness

The concept of mindfulness is over two and a half thousand years old and is part of Buddhist teachings. The ability to pay attention to a moment in time and gain insight from it is done through focusing on your breath in an intentional manner. This promotes and supports openness, awareness and acceptance.

Buddhist teachings refer to the bustling commotion of our minds as monkey mind. This apt description offers up an image of the frantic activity and noise that takes place in our heads on a daily basis. If the image of a monkey swinging from branch to branch with its shrill voice seems unfamiliar to you, then perhaps that of a hamster on a wheel or a flea in a bottle will fit.

The energy and aliveness of all these animals is to be admired, so the aim is not to banish the monkey (or hamster or flea) or to force it under control, but to gently quieten its frenzy.

Focused attention

The term meditation is frequently associated with sitting half-clothed and cross-legged in a trance-like state. Within the context of mindfulness work and this book, meditation refers to focusing attention on your most automatic of functions i.e. your breathing, in a way that harnesses your ability to attend to, and manage, yourself as you move through life.

Mindfulness, as a Buddhist practice, has crossed the east–west divide and found a valuable place amongst scientists and professionals, as well as many others. The benefits of meditation, which accompanies a practice of mindfulness and with which it is interwoven, are being researched and demonstrated in arenas such as helping people cope with symptoms of anxiety, depression, stress, chronic pain, addictions, hypertension, fibromyalgia, chronic fatigue, chronic heart disease, arthritis and cancer, amongst others (reading material is provided in a bibliography).

Coupling mindfulness with psychological awareness provides the opportunity for individuals to consider their lives and choices, and to take responsibility for these in a welcoming and respectful manner.

It is important to note that this is not a cure for medical or psychological conditions, but it is a process that can assist in the management of symptoms associated with them.

Pay-offs and sacrifices

Developing a mindful approach to life encourages a fuller and more active experience of life events, for whatever they are. It supports awareness of your breathing and physical movement, as well as your mental and emotional processes. This in turn develops your resilience and capacity to deal with the complexities of everyday life.

It allows you to create a greater skill of being present within the immediacy of your experiences, helping you to both accept them and to use your own skills and resources to enjoy or manage them.

> A mindful approach looks to emphasise and expand your own abilities rather than to assume that something external will make a difference.

The difficult part is that it requires practice and a willingness to attend to your life. It encourages being open to your emotional and mental worlds and to consider the choices you make in your life, as you are responsible for them.

Getting involved in your life

Paying attention to your life fosters greater engagement within it. It shifts the focus from getting through life to getting involved with it.

To be mindful involves being watchful, careful and respectful, and to be compassionate is to show kindness, consideration and care. When combined, there is a pronounced sense of treading caringly and carefully. So, developing a respectful caring for yourself can do no harm.

As individuals, we are perfectly imperfect. If we continue to avoid, deny and hate our imperfections we then need to narrow the range of vision of ourselves and our lives. If we keep running away from what we dislike about ourselves then we cannot stop long enough to enjoy the things that we might like.

Hard-sell life

Media and other influences can often lead us to believe that life is all about success and pleasure, rather than acknowledging the often harsh and painful realities of it. The message is that everyone is capable of everything and that the pursuit of success and pleasure is paramount, regardless of the cost to yourself or others. The emphasis is on getting, having and doing, leaving little room for our more vulnerable sides, such as feelings of hopelessness, fear or shame. Consequently, people often feel inadequate or ashamed that they are not matching up to a perceived image of success or perfection.

Cultivating a practice of mindfulness can help you to adopt a more sensitive and gentle approach to life and towards yourself. With its tone of tolerance and kindness, it allows you to recognise and accept your imperfections and humanness, with all its complexities.

Making choices

We do not always choose what comes our way, but what we do with it and who we wish to be are our choices. As individuals, we make decisions every day about our behaviour, values and reactions. We can either do this in a mindless and conditioned manner without giving it thought or consideration, or we can be mindful and aware, and bring attention and respect to it.

Every choice you make has a consequence.

The difficulty is that you don't always know what the consequence will be as it may only become evident many years later.

As you learn to be mindful, you will promote your ability to move through life with a more considered approach rather than being in overdrive or behaving in an unthinking or reactive manner. This does not mean that it is easy or that it will happen simply because you want it to. What it does is open the way to be actively aware and engaged in your interactions with yourself and with others. It encourages focused attention in order for it to be alive within each moment of your life – and it takes a lifetime of one moment joined to the next in order for it to happen. There is no end goal: it is like breathing – it needs to happen breath after breath, until your last breath.

Reflections in a shop window remind me of life

I am yet I am not.
My reflection to the world hides itself from me
as mine does to the world.
I look at my form as it flits past the shop windows
wanting to know what I see.
I look back at myself reaching out to take hold
but I have moved
moved on, moved away
without my reflection,
leaving behind what was and no longer is.
The shadows and shapes flicker inside my head
my eyes seeking me out.
I keep walking, watching each reflection
wondering where I had gone.

Anyone at home?

This book is about coming home to yourself by creating a way of being that is communicated at every level, and that is far beyond any cognitive or rational explanation. Mindfulness is a quality or essence that precedes words or reasoning, thereby making it more of an experience than a thought or explanation.

It lies deep within us as an instinctual attention and awareness that one can see in young children, before they are moulded into the belief that thought and logic are more important qualities to develop than those of emotions and kindness, particularly towards oneself.

Being mindful entails being in a state of awareness that recognises the experience of the moment prior to attaching words to it. It is similar to those fleeting moments when you stir from a night's sleep – no words, no thoughts, no logic – simply the experiencing of a state of being. Such a state is still reality but it hasn't been processed or organised.

Switching on not switching off

Imagine you are looking at a landscape painting in a room and what you see is a canvas within a frame hanging on a gallery wall, and you standing two feet away viewing it in a distant and objective state. You appreciate the tremendous skill of the artist, but there is no emotional stirring within you. Your mind then switches to a scenario where you are no longer an objective observer in the room, but are now in the picture – you smell the flowers, you feel the air against your skin, your senses light up to the variations of colour and texture, and even though you are not one of the objects within the original painting, it has become alive to you as you have to it. This is one aspect of mindfulness.

Developing mindfulness involves re-activating that original capacity to experience an experience as it occurs, in the way that it occurs, for whatever it is. Watching a toddler engrossed at the sight and touch of a miniature daisy or an ant is a powerful and pure example of mindfulness.

At home

People make choices, regardless of the events, and what mindfulness can do is allow you to take a breath before acting so that the choice can be a decision rather than a reaction. Increasing your mindfulness, and the practices that assist in this, is like switching your life from standby to active, from monochrome to multi-colour, from restriction to freedom.

It is about engaging with your life rather than observing it, as one day moves to the next. Being mindful not only incorporates a greater awareness of what is bright and pleasurable, but it can help make those moments more wonderful and the harsh and devastating times more bearable.

Right here right now

Perhaps it is now time to be at home, to be right where you are at this very moment. What was is gone and it is only the now of this moment that you have. It is unrealistic to believe that you can forget your past or deny your feelings, for you are today because of all that has brought you to this moment.

> The challenge is to allow both past and present to co-exist, so that the past does not overshadow the present, and the present is able to be real in its own right.

There are many aspects to life and to our existence as human beings. There is so much to know about and to learn that one can feel overwhelmed or even inadequate. However, sometimes what we already know is plenty, and all we need to do is to sit quietly and pay attention to it in a respectful and dignified manner.

A Tiny Piece

He left a tiny piece of himself with me
and then retreated into his world of shattered dreams.
I left a piece of myself with him
which no-one had seen before
and I was scared
Scared that someone may like it
So scared that the fragile strand would fade.
Foolishly, anxiously, I stepped towards him
believing he might want to see more.
His words had been kind and gentle,
soothing my fears of many years.
My heart, scarred and battered, began to smile
And it was in that moment that silence spoke of the hope
that someday
somehow
I would soothe my fears
and let myself walk towards the light.

Book Outline

Section 1   How Did I Get To Be Like This?

This section provides a brief discussion on how our genes, family lives, environments and inner worlds contribute to who we are at this moment, and why we develop as different and specific individuals.

Section 2   Paying Attention

The pace of everyday living, the extent of demands on us, and the quantity of information available have contributed to us speeding through our lives, forgetting at times to pay attention to them.

Section 3   Remembering your Body

Section 1 looked at people within a context. The focus now shifts to paying attention to the physical body.

Section 4   One Whole not Two Parts

The past four hundred years have promoted an idea that the mind and body are separate parts that have little or no connection. This chapter reminds us that we are a single, integrated and very complex unit.

Section 5   The Life of Breath

The ultimate importance of our breath is frequently overlooked – if we aren't breathing we aren't living. If our breath is what allows us to be alive, then paying attention to it may bring with it other advantages.

Section 6   Blocks and Barricades

We may start out with the best of intentions, but somewhere along the line we can become disillusioned, bored or dismissive. This issue is discussed and how such responses may become hindrances in our lives.

Section 7   Let's Go For a Walk

Awareness of walking through your world in different ways is considered in this section.

Section 8   Stopping

When we stop distracting ourselves from ourselves we can then move behind the smokescreens and assess our lives with clarity.

Section 9   Me and Me

To walk alone amongst many companions. This section looks at the fear of aloneness and the impermanence of life, but it also looks at how we can adapt to, and engage with, the transience of life.

Section 10   One Breath at a Time

Addressing attachments, looking at our fears, and learning to take life one breath at a time is the focus of this section.

Section 11   No Conclusion

Exactly what it says.

Concepts and Practices

The choice is yours whether to approach this book
with an open mind and a willingness to try
something different, or to dismiss it.

The only expectation is that which you bring.

The various sections outline how individuals tend to develop, and offer progressive steps towards cultivating a practice of mindfulness.

The Book

It is suggested that you read through each section consecutively as one leads on to the next. It can be done at your own pace as there is no time-scale attached to it. Once you have completed the book, you can select which components work best for you and continue with those. Some people find that the Body Focus routine helps when their bodies are tense and in pain, whilst others find the Mindful Awareness practice assists in keeping perspective and focus when they are agitated, stressed or troubled. Use whichever practice you think may be useful at a specific time.

The Practice

Work Choice and CDs: Work Choice isn't homework because you can decide whether or not to do it, but it is a step towards paying attention to your life and creating an anchor in it.

Listening to the CDs is optional, as with the Work Choice. However, they are the cornerstone of mindfulness and focusing on your breath, and have an intrinsic value. It would be helpful if you listened to each practice at least once in order to experience it. Thereafter, it is your choice.

Notes to Myself: This heading appears at the end of each section as an opportunity for you to record (or make a mental note of) your responses as you proceed through the sections.

Flickety-flick

There is always the temptation to flick through a book, listen to a few minutes of a CD and then put it to one side to gather dust. What is even more tempting is to flip through and tell yourself that you don't have the time to do it, but maybe you'll get around to it one day when things are different. That is what most people tend to do.

One way of overcoming this common practice is to find something within each section that interests you – something that tickles your curiosity or scratches at a sore patch. Once you have an interest in what you are doing, you then give yourself the impetus to go a step further.

> *What is so unimportant about your life that you cannot give it any time?*

IMPORTANT

At times of stillness feelings, thoughts or memories may come to the fore as the usual distractions ease away. Should this happen, acknowledge what it is without doing anything specific with it. If it is distressing, then be aware of the sensation but seek out some helpful way to manage these feelings. For example, take a walk in the garden or switch on the radio. Be careful not to engage in your usual way of managing distress if it involves anything harmful or negative. For some, the memories or emotions may be particularly distressing or hurtful, so it may be beneficial to talk to someone about them, looking to a qualified professional if necessary.

Therapy shouldn't be regarded as something frightening or embarrassing. It is a time when two people come together to try and understand you and your life, and to help take care of it.

There is no value in trying to block out what is emerging through the use of aggression, substances, sex or work. Avoiding your feelings and reactions only serves to perpetuate the damaging cycle that you may already be in. Feelings are there because of something that has taken place in your life, and there is no shame in having feelings.

What is important is that you seek support in a productive way. Memories and feelings don't disappear no matter how hard you may try to extinguish them – they only find different routes to be expressed. Pay attention to them and to the choice you make regarding how you deal with them.

What the conscious mind forgets
the unconscious remembers.

Section 1 – How Did I Get To Be Like This?

THE EVOLUTION OF MAN

The following chapter will outline how life impacts on our development, how our experiences add to who we are at this given moment, and a few examples of what we do as people in order to manage and survive, even as children.

Change is difficult, very difficult, so the question is can we change? Perhaps a more realistic word to use is shift. You can shift the way you think and feel, you can shift your actions and approach, but before this you need to understand what it is you feel, where it comes from, and why you want to shift it. Once these aspects begin to take shape, and there is sufficient discomfort for you, only then are you in a better position to negotiate yourself and the difficulties, and to move forward. It is when you are motivated for the right reasons to adjust a feature of yourself or your life that the process can begin. In addition, it takes and needs time and repeated experiences of trial and more trial in order for it to become integrated into your life.

> *You cannot turn rocks into rivers or trees into streams – each is its own.*

We often know things in our heads, but their true impact is felt when they are experienced at an emotional level. Insight gained only at a thought level is, in terms of change, a cognitive exercise, for if we changed every time we came across a piece of information that rang true for us then change would be effortless and immediate.

Start at the beginning

Our foundations are laid in our earlier lives, just like a sapling will develop and grow depending on the weather conditions, the quality of the soil and the support it receives. It will always be an oak, but its shape and health will be determined by the environment when it was most vulnerable. We are no different as people. We become who we are because of a combination of our genetic makeup and our environments, but who we wish to be and the way in which we conduct ourselves is then up to us.

As previously mentioned, you don't wake up one morning and decide to be stressed, bullied or addicted. By the same token, neither do you wake up one day and decide to be calm, healthy or philanthropic. Experiences, time and choices are usually what bring about a state of being, whether it be one of stability or one of chaos. Just as there is no quick-fix, there is no quick-cause. Events may occur in an instant, but our personalities take a lot longer to develop.

We are human – complex and complicated

An individual is a system of infinite layers of complex and interrelated structures, both physical and psychological. As a species, we are geared towards survival and self-preservation at all levels, so we develop mechanisms and filters, and we build protective fences (defences) in order to survive and cope with experiences.

23

These mechanisms continue to be used often long after the original anxiety has passed, and it can become part of our general way of dealing with life. For example, as a child one may have used silence as a means of survival or protection if caregivers tended to shout at and undermine the child. This form of coping becomes activated in each situation, and is then reinforced over time as being a successful tool to prevent being the target of antagonism or criticism.

As one encounters more life experiences which may not actually present as threatening but are reminiscent of earlier events, the perception or assessment of the situation is that it is one of threat. When this occurs, the coping structure automatically kicks into action.

It is helpful to remember that such devices arise as a means of coping with anxiety, as a defence is a tool developed in order to defend against an anxiety of some sort, such as fear of criticism, or anxiety that one will be physically hit or humiliated.

Self-protection and barriers

Defences are there in order to protect us from being overwhelmed by feelings or reactions that were felt to be frightening, and they are created at an unconscious level. Certain characteristics that are regarded as part of our nature can be traits that have, in fact, developed in childhood rather than being a temperament with which we were born.

Individuals do have different temperaments, and this is evident even in infancy, but other attributes may have begun life when the child was at his or her most vulnerable and least able to make sense of a situation. These characteristics developed in order to function within that scenario and to manage the perceived anxiety. The word *perceived* is used rather than *actual*, as the child, or adult for that matter, can only interpret the situation within his or her means at that time.

Our perception is like a pair of glasses. If you walk into a room that has a table and chair, a lamp and a bed, but the tint of the lens is black, then the room and all the objects will appear dark in colour. However, if the black lenses are replaced with pink ones when viewing the room, then the colour of it and the objects will now appear to have a pink hue to them. The room and objects have not changed, but the colour of the lens has influenced the individual's perception of them.

We all have our own lenses through which we perceive ourselves and the world around us, and they are moulded by our experiences. It may not always have been the incidents (e.g. being ignored) that left their mark but the underlying messages we extracted from them (e.g. I have no value because if I did this person would respond to what I'm saying).

We all need fences

It is necessary for people to develop ways of coping, and our encounters with life shape our perception. There is no set way in which we respond to experiences or how we react to circumstances. As adults, we can also build fences around ourselves for protection, but this is sometimes done in a more conscious way. A central issue is trust. If we have been able to trust our mothers and fathers (or primary caregivers) to protect us, meet our emotional and physical needs, and provide us with sufficient security, love and appropriate boundaries, then we believe we can trust ourselves and the world. This allows us to give and to receive more freely.

If our younger years were out of balance, then it becomes more difficult to believe that we are lovable and worthwhile, and much more difficult to believe that others might find us lovable and worthwhile. The two most important people in a child's world are his or her parents, even if one or both aren't around – all else evolves from thereon. Influential caregivers are like gas central heating systems. We anticipate that they will function adequately and provide warmth. Occasionally, they may break down and require maintenance and repairs which allow them to continue their tasks. It is when they malfunction and the gas begins to leak that they can become toxic. This also holds true for partners, siblings, friends and even colleagues.

If a parent is undermining and critical, then it is more likely that the child will always be more sensitive to criticism or what may be perceived as criticism. If someone has been abused, then he or she may either believe that others are allowed to cross the boundaries and abuse them, or else be over-alert to any possible abuse and keep people at a distance. By the same token, if the environment during childhood and adolescence was encouraging and respectful, then there is a greater possibility that the person will feel wanted and secure.

Children frequently infer, incorrectly, that incidents or situations are due to either a behaviour or characteristic of theirs. They cannot distinguish between what the issues are for the parents or what has happened without reason, and what is their doing. For example, a child may believe that his parents divorced because he didn't gain a place on the football team, or that her mother died because she had a fight with her.

As adults, there appears to be no logic in this, but children can only understand the world as children, because that is what they are. They see the world from a child's perspective and not from an adult's one, but adults tend to forget this. Imagine being a six-foot tall adult talking to another six-foot tall adult. Things are equal. Now shrink and imagine being a two-foot tall child staring up at a six-foot tall adult. The view is very different. It is this view that is often carried through from childhood into adulthood, and that remains as the foundation upon which we build a relationship with ourselves and others.

Adolescence or early adulthood may provide opportunities that rebalance some of the disruptions from earlier years, as it is then that individuals begin to be more involved with a wider variety of peers and life experiences. Achievements, relationships or circumstances may assist in negotiating around our beliefs, and allow us to move forward in our lives in a more positive and optimistic way. For some, however, events may have cut too deep, leaving behind wounds that never quite heal enough and tend to interfere with achieving desires and aspirations. There are always scars, whether they be thin and faded or harsh and swollen.

It is when your coping strategies outlive their original purpose and interfere in your everyday functioning or relationships that you need to become aware of them, and to make the links between the original circumstances that activated them and how they are now being used in your life and interactions.

Behind the mirror

It is easy to idolise or demonise people, but seldom do we get to see below the surface and to hear of the pain and despair beneath the headlines. As individuals, we are propelled to act as we do for a reason, with the most powerful force coming from the unconscious part of ourselves. Our drives and desires, as well as our thoughts and actions, are fuelled by it. What we know and recognise about ourselves at a conscious and rational level can be likened to the external shape and colour of a car, but it is the design of the engine and its power that propels it, just as our unconscious drives us.

The fact that our actions come about for a reason does not necessarily excuse them, but it does remind us that we are all capable of many things. It is about moving the unconscious into the conscious by paying attention to our desires and actions, making some sense of them if we can, or at least putting them into a context, and then mindfully choosing where to go from here.

People are not born bad or evil. Their actions come about from deep-rooted feelings that have become distorted and are then turned against themselves or others. It is not a straightforward cause-and-effect process, but usually a set of circumstances over a prolonged period of time that combine and multiply. Life changes us as its conditions and experiences mould and shape us.

Family situations and expectations, parental characteristics, educational and social opportunities and the individual's own temperament and experiences will encourage a certain path to be taken. For some, drugs or alcohol are abused, and this can exacerbate an already unstable situation limiting their ability to keep their lives in control, just as gambling or the need for power can. Misuse of power, emotional abuse or bullying are no different from physical violence, it's just that the scars can't be seen. For others, they have managed through opportunities and choices to curtail the more challenging parts of themselves and they take different paths.

> Life isn't perfect and it never will be
> because that's the way life is.

We are feeling beings, not just thinking beings. People have feelings because that's what comes with being human. You can only explain your actions, or reactions, by understanding the feelings that are the driving force behind them. For example, why does a small, and often insignificant, comment from person 1 result in person 2 exploding into a fit of anger? The comment, such as, 'That was a silly thing to do' may in itself have been said as a casual remark by person 1, but for person 2 it is like a knife that stabs straight into his feelings of inadequacy and incompetence. It is more than likely that such feelings developed in his earlier years and have remained with him. He may outwardly appear confident and competent, but it is his deeper and more vulnerable beliefs that triggered his angry response.

Repetition

People have a tendency to repeat the patterns of belief that were established early in life. This can continue throughout someone's lifetime without changing for two reasons. First of all, that pattern (of thought, feeling or behaviour) is so familiar that we continue doing it even when the outcome is painful or distressing. We know what to expect, we know how we'll feel, so we repeat it because we know how to deal with it. For example, a man may continually be attracted to partners who undermine him. He repeats this pattern, albeit unconsciously, as he knows how to feel bad about himself, and he is all too familiar with self-doubt and veiled anger. Should he choose a partner who praises his efforts and acknowledges his worth, then he is forced into unknown territory which can evoke great anxiety and raise too many questions about the origins of his beliefs. Consequently, the familiar route becomes the safe route.

The second reason we tend to repeat patterns is because at some level we hope that one day the outcome will be different, and that we will feel pleasure rather than pain. Somewhere we believe that if we try harder, work harder and keep at it, the result will be in our favour. Sadly, this is seldom the case and all that happens is that the bad feelings we have about ourselves are reinforced, not because they are true, but because we believe that the outcome proves it.

Having hope is beneficial if it gives you the impetus to work towards your goal or objective. It isn't necessarily helpful if you draw on it as though it has some specific power that will result in you magically having your wish fulfilled without any effort. For example, if you want to be an accountant you usually hope that the desired outcome will be achieved if you study hard i.e. that you pass your exams and qualify. On the other hand, if a partner is physically violent or emotionally abusive towards you, you can hope that he or she will change but hope isn't going to make the violence stop. You have to take action so that you can extricate yourself from the situation in order to keep yourself safe. In essence, it's important not to confuse hope with hard work.

If you do what you've always done, you'll get what you've always got. You can't do the same thing and expect a different outcome.

If you put your hand on a hot stove it will get burnt. If you don't want your hand to get burnt then don't put it on a hot stove. You can't put your hand on the stove and expect it not to get burnt.

Parents and significant others act as role models to children, and those children then tend to act in the same manner when they are adults. History does repeat itself because no matter how much people dislike a behaviour that was imposed upon them, they will frequently go on to impose it on others. There is no mystery to this. We do what was done (and role-modelled) to us because it is familiar so we know how to manage it. Alternatively, when we were the frightened or sad child who hated being abused or undermined, the feelings became so intolerable that one way to survive them was to take on (at an unconscious level) that characteristic of the person whose behaviour we found so difficult. By doing this, the anxiety created by the intolerable feelings is reduced, and so the behaviour is repeated by the next generation. For example, if a parental figure is a bully then the child takes on that behaviour as it is less frightening to be a bully than to manage the feelings of fear created by the parent's behaviour.

> History does not need to be repeated.

What can also happen is that we cut off the parts of ourselves that we don't like, such as our feelings of aggression or our fear of intimacy, and we disown them. One option is to then place those disowned emotions onto another person and perceive him or her as being aggressive or rejecting. Another option is to channel them into something more functional, such as taking up a sport. However, there are different ways in which we deal with our unwanted feelings, and many variations on how we set up situations in life to reinforce our beliefs about ourselves.

If you stop and consider why you feel and act as you do, you can then work with that knowledge and shift how you go about your life. You can change history. By listening to yourself and to others, and by paying attention to those things, you can gain greater understanding about your bright and wonderful facets as well as the dark shadow ones. All those parts are you, not just the bits that you pick and choose. It is by knowing them and integrating them into one whole that can allow you to be more aware and accepting of yourself. You may not be able to remove or obliterate what hurts, but you most certainly can do something about it and move forward with your life.

Distressing events in adulthood

Difficult times and distressing events also occur when we are adults. How we tend to deal with these events often depends on our personality structures and resources. We are like buildings. If a building has been constructed in a sound and solid manner, then it is far more resilient when the hurricane comes along. As individuals, when crises hit then it is those internal structures that will help us to either manage them over the long term, or leave behind severe and lasting damage.

Loss or damage can evoke powerful and ruthless emotions that can leave us feeling as if our very core has been stripped bare. At times we grieve for the loss of what we had, but at other times we may mourn the loss of what we never had. For example, if your mother was always critical of you, her death may leave you feeling sad but it could also stir up great sorrow as now the hope and fantasy that one day your relationship could be kinder is removed forever.

> What we feel will always come out in some form whether it be through an emotional or a physical channel.
>
> There is no getting away from it.

Emotional experiences and body memory

The work done in the field of neuroscience (i.e. the scientific study of the brain and nervous system) continues to reveal much evidence of how the mind and body function as one unit, and how experiences of both a physical and a psychological nature lodge themselves within our brains.

Pleasurable feelings produce chemicals and brain (neuronal) pathways within us just as difficult or traumatic experiences lodge themselves within the pathways of our brains. Consequently, the reactions found from highly stressful situations or the claims of benefits from meditation are no longer obscure beliefs but are increasingly gaining scientific support.

Keeping perspective

In a world that insists upon hard facts and science to verify existence, it is humbling to remind ourselves that life managed to exist for billions of years before scans and television came into being. We have played a part in understanding the extraordinary processes of life, but it is helpful to remind ourselves that we didn't create them.

Hype and pressure

Approaching life in a manner that only focuses on positive thinking and heroic determination restricts our humanness. We cannot always be upbeat, high achieving and in total control of our success, relationships and health.

Life happens, and we are vulnerable to its variations and determinants from the moment of conception. Many factors have some bearing on our development, such as the physical, emotional or psychological state of the mother, the couple's attitudes and situations, stress, support, and financial or social conditions. Each set of factors influences and shapes who we are today and what has brought us to this point.

Looking for ways out

At times we believe that we cannot rely on ourselves to get us through life as we assume we are the problem, and this can lead to feelings of self-loathing, anger and despair.

Many people start to look for something beyond themselves for help, but some may become problems in their own right, such as drugs, risk-taking, alcohol or crime (including white collar ones, such as fraud and irresponsible business deals). Others, however, may provide a route that can encourage kindness and acceptance of oneself and one's experiences, and offer up possibilities that are supportive and enhancing. Mindfulness is one of these.

Choice

We cannot stop the sea ebbing and flowing or the rain falling, but we can decide if we wish to be kind or critical, loving or selfish. You may need to work at understanding yourself, but that too becomes your choice.

Everyone has a past, and no childhood or upbringing is perfect. Many people have good enough or even lovely childhoods, so not everyone experienced trauma or disruption. However, for some, aspects of their lives may have evoked anxiety or left them feeling particularly vulnerable. This is often hidden from others, and sometimes even from themselves, but it will show itself in other ways such as in depression or cynicism, even in the face of something being offered that could hold the possibility of being helpful or different.

Intentional awareness allows us to focus on the world within ourselves and the world around us. It provides an opportunity to use our selves as an anchor and stabiliser when life moves from one moment to the next. It encourages both involvement and separation. It challenges beliefs that restrict our living life in a manner that permits choice, control and freedom in the complex and multifaceted world within and around us.

> Integrity is about taking responsibility not only for the choice you make but also for the consequences of it.

Work Choice

The following exercises introduce you to the idea of paying attention to yourself.

(a) Sensations Exercise: – take a piece of food, such as a section of fruit or a piece of chocolate. Place it in your mouth and very slowly and carefully chew it, taking one or even two minutes in which to complete the task.

- Notice the taste and texture of the object in your mouth, as well as the physical sensations as you slow down the movements of your jaw and tongue.

- Become aware of what is going through your mind whilst carrying out this task.

(b) Stillness Exercise:

Sit still for 2 minutes –

- Notice what sensations are in your body, such as an urge to move, pain in your shoulder or the need to scratch your leg.

- What thoughts are going through your mind as you sit?

this is me ... is this me?

Notes to Myself

Section 2 – Paying Attention

To do, and what to do next, has replaced the debate of how to be or who to be. We are constantly active – we bathe, dress, eat, work, play, shop, travel, and we do most of it without paying much attention to it or to the consequences of it.

Paying attention to your life differs from being over-involved in every detail of it. Being alert and alive within your own life is about switching on to it, being in it, and knowing what is going on even if it isn't something that feels good. It's not about being self-absorbed. You are the centre of your own existence, and you need to take responsibility for that existence, but you are part of a greater unit that shifts and changes over time. Your importance is not diminished by this but rather is held within the perspective of life being a transient and impermanent state.

Forgetting ourselves

Age, demands, current trends, personal desires and social and parental attitudes can often lead us to lose touch with ourselves – our instincts, bodies and feelings, our sensations and senses, and even with the core of who we are and what we represent. Perhaps one of the greatest injustices imposed is that of being led to believe that we are unlovable and unworthy, and to feel shame about ourselves, for it is that that leads on to manifest itself in so many other states, be it depression, self-loathing, jealousy, greed, murderous rage, hopelessness, prejudice, eating disorders, self-mutilation, panic attacks, heart attacks, substance misuse and countless others.

Intentional awareness is what it says – it is about knowingly paying attention to the experiences within and around us at this given moment, within a context of respect, compassion and kindness. In this way, it allows us to become familiar with our fragility and vulnerability, as well as our remarkable resilience and robustness.

Work Choice

a) Do one activity in your day, each day, in a focused and attentive manner. Examples of activities are washing your hands, drinking a cup of tea, washing dishes, walking to the car, getting dressed or undressed, chopping vegetables, watering the garden.

Pay full attention to the activity, noticing sensations aroused such as taste, touch or smell. Observe where your mind goes and the distractions to which you respond. Be aware of your breathing and the changes that occur as you focus on the task.

(b) Two-Minute Breathing Concentration Exercise:

Sit in a chair and with your eyes open or closed –

–   Breathe in silently counting 1, 2, 3, 4 and then breathe out silently counting 1, 2, 3, 4. (or 'in', 2, 3, 4 then 'out', 2, 3, 4). Repeat 5 times and do not force the breath.

- Breathe in for the same length of time as above but now silently counting 1, 2 and then breathe out for the same length counting 1, 2 (or 'in', 2; 'out', 2). Repeat 5 times, remembering not to force the breath in any way. Let if flow naturally.

- Breathe in without any counting, and breathe out without counting. If you find it difficult, then you can say 'in' for the duration of the in-breath, and 'out' for the duration of the out-breath.

Notes to Myself

Section 3 – Remembering your Body

The physical state and shape of our bodies keep many industries alive and profitable. There is a tendency to focus on what is portrayed as an ideal shape and on how perfectly our bodies should function. The reality is that our bodies are as vulnerable and prone to variations and disruptions as are our minds and emotions.

Chronic pain, illness or emotional distress frequently leads to imbalanced or distorted views of ourselves, including that of our bodies.

The emphasis in this section is on your physical existence, and this is done through the use of the Body Focus practice which can be found on one of the CDs.

Body Focus Practice

Time and Place

Finding a time and place to carry out the practices is the greatest challenge. Let your phone be turned off or on silent mode and ask others not to interrupt you unless it is an emergency.

It is possible to create a reasonably quiet place and space around yourself if you are willing to set limits and establish some boundaries. You are allowed to do this – this is your life.

Positions

Lying Flat. It is preferable to lie on your back on the floor (use a mat or blanket if there is no carpet). Place your legs on a chair, either straight or bent, if that is easier on your back. You can also lie on a bed or any flat surface if getting onto the floor is difficult.

Sitting in a Chair. If lying down is uncomfortable or difficult then sit in a chair. When sitting, it is important to check that the chair is high enough so that your knees are not higher than your hips. The chair should provide sufficient support, but again use footstools or cushions if necessary. Try not to be slumped in the chair.

Standing. If neither lying nor sitting are comfortable then lean against a wall or stand, but take care that you have a firm object against which to steady yourself.

Clothing

Keeping Warm. Wear sufficient clothes or cover yourself with a blanket as your body temperature will cool.

When the instruction says 'breathe into your hip' or any part of your body, it is about imagining that your breath is able to reach that part. Physiologically, we cannot breathe into any part of the body other than the lungs, so breathing into your toes or abdomen is about doing so in your mind's eye. By placing the breath, in your imagination, into a specific area it helps to focus attention on it and to ease the tension within that area.

It's not about having the time
it's about having the commitment.

42

Work Choice

(a) Listen to the Body Focus practice.

(b) Questions to ask yourself.

- Did you make the time and privacy to do the work suggested?

- What was it like doing it?

  your concentration during the task

  the sensations and discomforts that arose in your body

  were there any feelings of anxiety or pleasure that arose?

(c) What happens to your body when you are distressed by physical or emotional difficulties?

- Where in your body do you feel it?

- What sensations do you feel in your body at that time?

- Where is that feeling right now?

- Has the physical pain led to an emotional response (e.g. irritation, depression etc.), or has the emotional distress triggered a physical reaction (such as stomach ache, difficulty in breathing or a headache) or a craving for a drug/alcohol/food?

- What thoughts come into your mind at times like this?

Any links?

- How do you cope with physical sensations?

- How do you cope with emotional arousal?

- Is there any link between what you are feeling physically, your emotions and your thoughts? For example, if your back is aching and you need to lie still do you become irritable, which leads to your shouting at your partner, which in turn leaves you feeling guilty and ashamed?

- What do you do when you feel this way?

- Does the action work i.e. does taking a pill, going for a walk, having a drink, shouting at someone, or the like, achieve what you want it to?

Notes to Myself

Section 4 – One Whole not Two Parts

Our physical development is what takes centre court when we are infants. The belief is held that infants and young children do not remember events, incidents or situations and that it is only as they get older that they may recall or retain them. This view has distorted the importance that early life experiences have on the emotional growth and expansion of the individual.

We remember more than we realise

Children use their instincts as their basis for survival and interaction, as the cognitive structures in the brain are still in the early stages of development and only complete their final phase around the age of 20, or later. This is somewhat surprising, as we tend to think of language and thinking abilities as being well developed by late adolescence. Part of the difficulty is that one cannot readily see the brain developing or the pathways that an emotional experience takes within it.

It is far easier to monitor a child's height, weight and ability to read or to run. Emotional and psychological indicators are often indirect and obscure, and are frequently overlooked or disregarded. However, because we have tended to view the physical development of an individual as being separate from, and unrelated to, the person's emotional development does not necessarily mean that it is correct.

Emotions precede thoughts

We feel long before we think or put words to our experiences. It is unlikely that a hungry infant debates the experience of hunger pangs, the activities of the caregiver or the availability of the food. The cry of extraordinary volume for one of such tiny size is based purely on arousal and need. We are physiologically and psychologically programmed to respond to emotions with the most primitive reactions of fight or flight.

Our bodies are automatically activated to undertake one or the other before our intellectual ability has time to assess the situation. If we hear a loud noise our bodies will immediately respond prior to us realising that someone dropped the tray on the kitchen floor. It may take a second or two before becoming aware of the cause of the noise, but our hearts are already beating within our chests and our limbs are in 'Go' mode.

From an emotional perspective, fight is not only the use of physical force but could be channelled into, for example, psychological aggression just as flight may not necessarily mean running away, but could include shutting down emotionally.

Fear comes in many colours

We are capable of a vast array of emotions, whether we acknowledge them or not. Fear is fundamental to our survival but it also seeps into other areas of our lives, such as fear of failure, of humiliation or of loss. We often fear our own emotions and possible reactions to them. We fear our anger and what we might be capable of doing if we let out the rage, we fear our sexuality as it may feel too powerful or lustful, we fear our despair in case others think us weak or we consider suicide, we fear our pain as it can feel unbearable but we are told to be strong and not to complain. At times, we fear not the emotion itself but how we might react to the intensity of it, whether it be pleasurable or obstructive.

We may also fear life as it is not always easy to bear the disappointment, rage, humiliation or shame that can come with it. Sometimes life can feel terrifying and there isn't always someone around to hold our hand. Even when the happenings in life are good, we can be scared to immerse ourselves in them in case something goes wrong or we worry we may be seen as greedy or brash.

Mind–body divide

The mind–body divide was upheld by many professionals and society as a whole for centuries, advocating that the mind and the body exist as two separate entities that just happen to exist within one container, the physical body. Frequently, those who sought to offer an alternative view were seen as tree-huggers who brewed potions from the woods and chanted at the moon. There is still that biased view even now when one uses the term meditation.

Many people have suffered the indignity of receiving, or not receiving, a diagnosis as it was regarded as being in their heads – as something that didn't really exist as it couldn't be clearly defined in physical terms. Fortunately, science and society have begun to close the divide although there is still some way to go in this area.

Nature and nurture

It is surprising that there are still debates as to whether we are the outcome of nature (our genetic inheritance and what we are born with) or nurture (the actions of our parents, caregivers, and the like). In essence, we are comprised of biological, psychological and social factors which are coupled with our life experiences, resulting in who we are today. No-one can stop the processes and changes of life, and because we are human it is inevitable that we will experience a large variety of events and emotions and react to them in various ways.

Nature + nurture = choice

We can neither overcome our genetic blueprint nor dismiss our experiences. What we can do is accept that we have a choice about how we conduct our lives. Being able to change our genetic history or childhood experiences would feel like less of a responsibility than knowing that we can make choices about what we do with our lives.

Many give little thought to the impact that making choices can have on their lives. We know we have the ability to make decisions but we may prefer to overlook the enormity of what it means to have free will … because if we do, then we are required to admit how often we opt out of the choice process, and opt in to the one of having no say. Of course, there is also the option of denying to ourselves the fact that we did have a choice but that it was easier to ignore it.

Feelings in the heart can become feelings in the body

Emotional struggles are frequently manifested in physical illnesses or discomforts (and vice versa) but if the mind and body are regarded as separate entities, then making the links or mapping the path of how one aspect impacts on the other becomes increasingly clouded and difficult.

If the divide is drawn together then it becomes easier to understand how, for example, anxiety can manifest itself in breathing difficulties, unhappiness in a relationship in skin or back problems, or anger in digestive problems. Physical pain can lead to depression, impotence to aggression. This is not to say that the one automatically leads to the other, or that a physical pain is simply an unresolved psychological issue. What it is implying is that people work as one system of interlinked mechanisms, that is mind and body, not mind or body. When the two are brought together then the issue in question can be addressed from appropriate angles.

There appears to be limited value in giving someone a new heart without paying attention to the stressors and lifestyle that may have contributed to the first one becoming so damaged. Stressors include the obvious, such as a busy job, but also matters such as poor self-esteem, working too hard to overcompensate for feelings of inadequacy or drinking too much alone late at night to blank out unhappiness.

Work Choice

(a) Continue with the Body Focus practice.

(b) Be aware of what happens around the practice – for example, do you have a set time, do you plan it, what goes through your mind when thinking about it, are you analysing things as you do it, what is the process around it?

The focus is on becoming aware of yourself, within a given moment, and not on a mental exercise.

Notice your response to approaching this task, and your response after you have completed it.

- After the practice, remain where you are and notice how you are breathing – is it shallow and harsh or deep and relaxed?

- Where does the breath go, where does it stop, what do you do with it, is it a pleasant or unpleasant sensation?

- How does your body feel at this moment?

- How do you feel right now?

Notes to Myself

Section 5 – The Life of Breath

Without breath there is no life. It is the ability to take in oxygen from the air and expel the toxins that sustains us. Your life exists from your first breath until your last, and we use those terms on a daily basis often forgetting that they are meant in a very literal way.

Your life consists of every breath you take between those two events, and each moment is a new moment of breathing. Meditation pays so much attention to what we take for granted, i.e. our breathing, because it is our life force. We talk of life-support machines, which are machines that allow individuals to remain alive even when they are functionally not able to do so on their own, and those machines are breathing machines.

Attending to your breathing is not about being taught how to breathe, but about learning to use your breath to your advantage. It is like walking – we can walk, but going for a walk is done with intent and purpose. In the same way, breathing in order to survive is one matter, but harnessing the force of your breath and using it to influence and strengthen your life can have a powerful impact.

Connecting breath and movement

Movement that is done in an aware and mindful manner (i.e. with intent) reminds us to attend to all parts of our bodies and not only the painful back, the heavy chest or the knotted stomach. It connects us to our physical selves, to our breathing and to the internal mechanisms that come with that.

Chronic pain, distress, depression, anger and a host of other factors contribute to us losing faith in our bodies. We often criticise our bodies which may feel fat, defective or tense, but for whatever they are, they contain not only the physical pains, scars and restrictions but all the emotional ones too.

Moving your body helps to mobilise it and to integrate the links between mind and body. Mindful movements allow the opportunity to carefully put in motion whichever parts you can, and it reminds you that you are a living and moving entity.

> The Body Movement practice is an important step in taking responsibility for your body.
>
> It requires being careful and accountable to yourself whilst focusing on the immediacy of the experience.

Work Choice

Take care.

Do not push yourself or do anything that may hurt or harm you in any way. If you are unsure, then please consult a professional.

Body Movement Practice

- Stand on a flat surface, preferably on a yoga mat.

- Do not stand on a loose rug or blanket as it is easy to slip.

- Wear comfortable clothing, removing any jewellery that may get entangled or hurt you.

- Take it slowly.

- This is not a competition.

- Be sensible – you know your body better than anyone else.

(a) Practise the Body Movement section, which is a gentle mobility routine. There is a 5-minute Gentle Space (track 7) between the Body Focus and Body Movement practices, which consists of silence interspersed with a bong sound.

(b) Questions

- What is your attitude to this task?

- Is there pain?

- How did/are you dealing with it?

- Are you being responsible with the moves?

- What happens to your mood during the routine?

- What happens to it after the routine?

- Did your mood affect your willingness to carry out the task?

- What was it like being aware of your body whilst it moved?

- What was your response to simultaneously being aware of your movement and your breath?

- Make a note of how you feel at different intervals, for example, two hours after the practice, at bedtime and the following morning.

(c) An Awareness Exercise

Pay attention to one event during the day, such as driving, eating, bathing, washing, sitting at the computer, attending a meeting, talking on the phone or any other ordinary event that occurs in your day. Notice what is happening to your body (e.g. posture, pain, tension), your breathing (shallow, forced, easy), your mood (stressed, depressed, anxious, angry, irritable, calm) and the way in which you interact with others at that point, if relevant (harshly, aggressively, kindly, timidly, fearfully).

Notes to Myself

Section 6 – Blocks and Barricades

Feeling indifferent to all this or debating whether or not to continue?

Scepticism is good

Resistance and scepticism are appropriate responses to something new and unfamiliar. These types of responses act as a means of protection of the current safety zone, or at extremes of our survival. Whether as a child or as an adult, one becomes accustomed to being told what to do and how to do it.

This direction may be offered in a spirit of helpfulness but when it is imposed upon one, especially if there is criticism or judgement attached to it, it will have a negative impact which can lead to poor self-esteem and becoming shut down to anything new.

Rigidity

Resistance to the unfamiliar has a place, but if that resistance is so rigid and prickly that it forces one to turn away from what may be of use then it could present itself as a problem. The choice is to either acknowledge and manage the resistance, or to walk away and reject what is being offered.

Connections

I met a man who touched my soul
as we passed in the darkness of looking for light.
His face was sad,
his eyes shuttered against the pain of his life.
His image showed both past and present,
his body the disillusionment.
I looked at him not knowing if he could lift the shutters of
protection.
He looked at me, his eyes talking of his withered soul.
Beneath the banter lurked our pasts,
our fingers touching in a moment of humour and hope.
Stepping out of my fear I moved towards him
but he was gone.
Waiting, I reached again, more hesitant than before,
but still he was gone.
A sadness descended upon me
as I looked in and felt the familiar pain of self-doubt and
confusion, critical and harsh.
My shutters groaned against the downward pull
for he was gone,
perhaps lost forever.

Feelings can be a nuisance

As you sit quietly away from the sought-after distractions that keep the distress at bay, the discomforts and realities of life may emerge. They may pop into your head as an image, come to you as a memory or a thought, or even leave you with a feeling of uneasiness you cannot quite identify. This is similar to the experience of people going on holiday in order to relax and have fun, only to find that the first few days are filled with feelings of, for example, depression, anxiety or tension, or they may become physically unwell.

Being open to support

Becoming involved in mindfulness and meditation is one form of support. However, if at any point the resistance or the emotional distress feels too powerful to deal with on your own, then it would be wise to discuss it with an appropriate individual so that you can be given support and direction on how to work with it. Sometimes putting our fears or angers into words, and telling someone else about them, helps to loosen their intensity. At other times, it is sensible to consider more ongoing or specialist support, such as seeing a therapist.

People have lives, and sometimes the experiences that come with those lives are difficult or destructive. There may have been countless good or neutral experiences, but there may also have been some that just weren't very pleasant or were blatantly traumatic. Life is tricky, so why jump out of a plane without a parachute if one is available?

No-one ever knows what has really gone on in someone else's life because no two people experience the same event in the same way, no matter whether they are born into the same family, are in the same accident, climbed the same mountain or attended the same dinner party. It is when our personal reality is denied that distress or conflict can arise.

Each person is a distinct and singular unit that cannot be reproduced because the millions of variables that have combined over your lifespan can never be replicated. You are who you are at this moment as a result of each of these specks of time.

We tend to do our best as individuals, whether on our own or as partners, friends or colleagues. However, when we know there is a difficulty that is affecting our own lives or those of others and we choose to do nothing about it, then we stop doing our best. At such times, we consciously and willingly choose to continue along this hurtful and damaging path regardless of the outcome.

Work Choice

(a) Practise the Body Movement or Body Focus routine (or both).

(b) What resistance might you be feeling regarding the ideas put forward so far?

- How good are you at taking responsibility for yourself and what goes on in your life, your head, and your heart? For example, do you feel used but refuse to set limits, or do you get irritable with others when you're annoyed with yourself for drinking too much the night before?

- How do you deal with experiences and emotions?

Make a note of an experience or event that has left an impression on you, whether recent or in the past.

- What is/was the experience or event?

- How did it come about?

- How did you respond?

- Why did you respond like that?

- What was the impact on you of responding like that?

- What was the impact on others of your responding in that way?

- What are/were the consequences?

- How mindful and aware were you of yourself when this experience occurred?

- How much do you try and avoid what's really going on?

Do you repeat the same experience and expect a different outcome?

Notes to Myself

Section 7 – Let's Go For a Walk

This part is an extension of the ideas found in Section 5. The emphasis is on participating in an activity that is commonplace for most people. The aim is to use walking as an example of approaching an ordinary activity in a different manner, although you may need to go through the 4 stages a couple of times in order to become familiar with the concepts.

When walking we often focus on getting from one point to another and seldom do we take the time to experience the sensation of it – the feel of the ground beneath our feet, the slow and rhythmic movement of the ankle and foot as it steps down and is raised up, the air against our skin.

1. To start, take a walk in the garden, in the park or anywhere that is convenient. Keep your eyes half closed and let the focus be on your internal experiences and sensations, and that of your body and mind. Keep the objects that surround you, such as other people or the trees, at a distance in your mind.

2. Having done that, lift your eyes and bring into your awareness all the objects and movements around you. Allow yourself to be open to all of these and how they impact on you. Attend to the detail of each object and how it is placed within that particular setting.

3. Now move the emphasis on to the place that you are holding within this environment and the impact that you are having on it. Let the cycle of your breathing become balanced and be an integral part of this mini world around you. Notice your

sensations, reactions and responses as you do this, and if they are different from how you normally would be within such a situation.

4. Finally, step back from such an active involvement and let there be a space between yourself and your immediate surroundings. Be aware of them and sensitive to them, but not fully a part of them. Again notice the difference in your sensations, feelings and thoughts.

Work Choice

The exercise above is one form of meditation, albeit in an adapted form. The practice of Mindful Awareness is now presented which looks to concentrate your attention whilst you are sitting or lying still.

Notes on Mindful Awareness

You can do this in whatever position is possible for you, but sitting helps you to stay awake. Your eyes can be open, half-closed, or closed depending on what feels safe for you. You may wish to start with them half-closed, and then as the practice becomes more familiar you can shut them. As previously mentioned, when there are instructions to breathe into a part of your body other than the lungs, it is about imagining the process of placing your breath into that area as if you are able to let the breath reach that part, such as your elbow or groin.

Listen to one of the Mindful Awareness practices each day. The longer version gives more detailed guidelines than the shorter version, so it is best to listen to the longer one at least once so that you can familiarise yourself with the routine. Thereafter, the shorter version can be used if this is preferred. A 5-minute version is also included, and there is a Gentle Space between each of the versions.

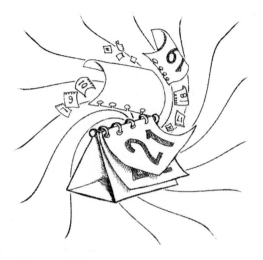

'Well, maybe later, if I find the time, when I've finished this project,
or one day when …'

The only way to do it is to do it.

Notes to Myself

Section 8 – Stopping

Life catches up with you

You can continue running or hiding from what you really feel, but it will always be there until you stop and face it. You can deny, avoid, ignore or dismiss it but that won't make it go away. All it does is drive you to push it out by using things like drugs, sex, sport or work. The more you run, the harder you need to run, but the monsters inside our heads are seldom as frightening when placed in front of us.

You are able to tolerate what you feel, and in time, the intensity will pass. More importantly, you can deal with it and you can stop hurting yourself and those around you. Denial about the effect it has on you, and about the effect you and your choices and behaviour have on others, can only lead to more pain and trouble.

Those feelings again

The difficulty with emotions is that they are shrouded by veils, and it can take time to lift those illusory coverings in order to identify what is at the centre of the struggle. An example of this is a person being depressed, which is commonly accompanied by a feeling of lethargy or restlessness. Depression, however, can be the flip side of anger, either with oneself or with someone else. The anger is too powerful or frightening to express, so it is converted into a more accepted form i.e. depression. The fire of the anger is suppressed and quelled, allowing its power to be turned away from the other person(s) and against oneself. The fear is that if the anger, or any other feeling, was to be released it would be destructive and damage the other person. Consequently, turning it against oneself becomes the safer and more socially acceptable route, in that person's mind.

Identify a difficult or distressing feeling that is occurring in your current life (or did in the past). Consider your immediate response to it, such as, 'I can't tolerate this feeling', 'I'll never be able to stop drinking', 'My life is a disaster', 'I'm such an idiot'. Approach the situation or feeling again but with the following in mind:

Be specific. Rather than saying 'My life is a disaster', break it down so that you can get to exactly what it is that has resulted in this feeling, and if you feel this way about all of your life or just one area of it.

> Just because you feel one thing doesn't mean you don't feel other things.
>
> For example, you may feel despair about the breakup of a relationship but you are still a competent person in the workplace.

Feelings co-exist

This means that you can feel depressed about one thing but also happy about another. You can feel humiliated by an incident at work and also proud of the function you held on the weekend. You can hate your partner and also love him or her. The one does not exclude the other, and it is important to hold on to the reality of both existing within you, rather than it being one or the other.

> Don't get trapped by the belief that now is forever.

Return to the feeling you previously identified and without delving into it or running from it simply allow it to exist. Recognise it for what it is (such as anger, hatred, fear, disgust) acknowledge it and then breathe into it.

Physically breathing into the area of pain (in your mind's eye) or when a craving or wave of emotion grips you helps to dissipate the intensity of it. Once the intensity has eased, find that part of yourself that feels solid and balanced, no matter how small, and breathe into it. Reassure yourself that this difficult experience will pass and that you can get through it.

Systems

Whatever you do to yourself will impact on you as a system, and whatever you do will impact on the system around you. We have a remarkable capacity to believe that what we do only affects us as individuals and that we can deal with it: we can take care of it and it doesn't impinge on our lives, families, friends or anyone. It's all under control.

> Tread carefully as you walk through the forest of life for it may be you underfoot.

Work Choice

(a) Listen to the Mindful Awareness practice each day (longer or shorter version).

no judgement, no expectation – simply being

(b) **A Time Line of Your Life:** Take a large piece of paper and draw a horizontal line across the centre of the page. At the start of the line on the left-hand side draw a dot and put your date of birth (e.g. 1960). Work your way across the horizontal line placing dots and what they indicate (e.g. 1963 family moved to a different city; 1969 failed exams; age 10 started being bullied; 1975 mother very ill; 1978 left home; 1982 depressed; 1984 met future partner; 1987 birth of child; and so forth) either above or below the line depending on whether the dot represents a positive or happy incident of your life, or a difficult or distressing one. The height or depth of the dot will indicate the extent of the impact of that event or period in your life. When this has been completed join the dots and observe the route of your life up to this point.

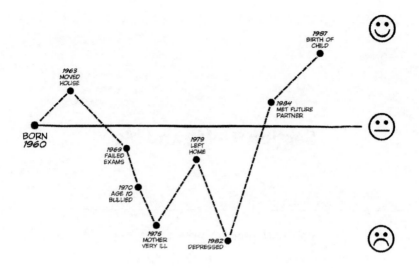

This activity will remind you of experiences both recalled and forgotten. It will place them within a timeframe and emphasise the context of events. For example, it may highlight the link between a series of losses and the marked increase in your working hours, which eventually led to the deterioration of your relationship and the development of health problems.

(c) Each morning, when you get out of bed, either sit on the side of the bed or stand next to it and consciously take a gentle but full breath and then release it. What happens when you take this moment to stop before launching into your day?

Notes to Myself

Section 9 – Me and Me

> You will face no greater ally or
> enemy in your life than yourself.

This section has been included because we are scared that if we stop the merry-go-round of being busy and distracted then all our fears and anxieties will jump out at us. The chances are that some will, but they often lose their intensity and power when we look them in the eye. Whether you turn towards yourself or run from yourself, either way you are still you.

Being alone with our pain and distress is no easy task, and life can be brutal at times. It is at these times that our shame, rage, fear, disappointments and all the batterings of life come together and echo relentlessly within us.

It is also at these times that the care and kindness of mindfulness can help you through the despair, not because it takes it away but because it helps you to focus on the core of you. It directs you to the mountain inside that can withstand the harshness of a bleak and desolate winter, and respond to the gentle warmth and brightness of the daffodils in spring.

The belief that the newness of each breath can sustain life, and detaching from the destructiveness of thoughts, knowing that they are transient and only thoughts, is what can hold your hand from this moment to the next.

shhh

It is late.
I beg to sleep
to shut out the silence of the night
for it is then that the voices of my hell begin to shout
to shriek, to shrill
to shatter the silence of the night
to pound at the strength of my sanity.

But tonight the monsters are quiet
they are still.
I breathe, listening, waiting
but they are still.
I breathe again, waiting.

They are quiet tonight, for tonight I feel a warmth within,
a flicker of relief for nothing other than for the stillness of
the night.

Things change

Situations are transient, life is impermanent, and people are fallible
and mortal. Suffering is part of being human as much as pleasure or
hunger. To deny this is to try and create a barricade around our innate
well of existence.

Things change in other ways too. Think back on a situation in the
past when you thought it would never be any different. The chances
are that it did change, in some way. Perhaps the feeling you originally
had has not disappeared altogether but you know that there have been
better and worse times, and lighter and darker periods, since then.
Also, if you felt one thing then it doesn't mean you have to feel the
same way now.

If you balance on one foot, it doesn't mean that you only have one foot and that the other doesn't exist. It's about acknowledging the shifts and altering perspective.

Reactions to life

Depression can be the other side of anger; bullying an overcompensation for feeling inadequate; overuse of drugs or alcohol a way to escape discomfort; overeating a seeking of comfort or a means of pushing down distressing feelings; high risk-taking an avoidance of the deadness inside; being domineering or controlling a means of counteracting feeling powerless in past situations; being brusque a way of keeping people at a distance.

Such reactions serve the purpose of attempting to change one's state of discomfort and to reduce the aroused feelings, but the relief is only temporary. Using such means doesn't change the reality, they only alter and distort it.

As has been said before, try as we may feelings will always find a way out in one form or another.

Symptoms not conditions

It may be the shame or hurt that we have about our experiences that leads us to be defensive, angry, fearful, hopeless, isolated or alone, and it is for these reasons that people turn to outside sources for comfort and escape.

Hurting yourself or others, in ways mentioned above, is usually a symptom rather than a condition. Underlying it is the pain we feel which is diverted into, for example, aggression, risk-taking and using drugs. Behaviours are not always an accurate indication of what is happening inside the person. A case in point is that men often present as agitated or belligerent when in fact they are suffering from depression. A further example, is that children can become overactive and seeking of attention when there is conflict between their parents in order to place the attention onto themselves, as a way of diverting the parents and deflecting the conflict.

We attempt to cover over the feelings with the likes of sex, pills and money or anything that we believe will help us to control the intensity and discomfort of what we are really feeling. It is only when we take an interest in who we are and what motivates us, with a sense of curiosity and understanding, that we can recognise these factors. Once we acknowledge them, we can allow ourselves the opportunity to accept and take responsibility for them, but without the use of things like alcohol or doughnuts.

A note on thoughts

Thoughts are just thoughts, even those desperate, hateful or shocking ones. They are part of you and come from within you, but they aren't all of you. On the Mindful Awareness CD there is a comment about not attaching yourself to your thoughts and simply letting there be a space between yourself and your thoughts. This is quite liberating. When you feel like your head is in a washing machine on high speed, step back in your mind and remind yourself that thoughts are only thoughts.

The mirror

Being mindful of all the goodness within yourself as well as your vulnerabilities and frailties, and accepting these different parts of yourself, allows for a more honest and real reflection to be seen in the looking-glass.

There are things that are within your control and there are things over which you had no control, no matter how good, caring, horrible, unkind or selfish you were as children or are as adults. It isn't always your fault.

Parents are sometimes horrible to their children no matter how hard the child tries to be lovable and worthy, and sometimes adults are horrible to each other. At times we may intend to be like that, and at other times we don't, but it still has an impact on us and those around us and there are consequences that arise from it.

Assets and liabilities

Our assets are often our liabilities – whereas it may be a good thing to be in control of ourselves and to be careful in whatever we do, the flip side is that we may be scared of letting go, of showing our true selves with all our qualities and imperfections.

We all mess up, make mistakes, and want to protect ourselves from criticism, but if there is an elephant in the middle of the room and everyone tiptoes around it pretending it isn't there, then the walk around the room is going to be a rather awkward and difficult one, and the atmosphere is not going to encourage trust and honesty.

An elephant in the middle of the room isn't hard to spot but it takes a great deal of energy to deny its existence.

Work Choice

(a) Listen to one version of the Mindful Awareness practice each day.

(b) Make a note of your three most powerful but difficult feelings or reactions (such as fear, self-hatred and jealousy) and your three most positive ones (such as kindness, generosity, and warmth). Do any of these relate to a specific incident or incidents within your life?

(c) What sets off these emotions? For example, a disappointment, being alone, a rejection, a friend in need, going on holiday?

(d) How do you manage them? Do they come out directly or have they found alternate and less direct ways of being expressed? For example, if you are angry with someone, do you tend to withdraw for fear that you will scream and lose control with him or her, or do you have a tendency to forget to do things that you have promised to do for that individual? Another example is when you feel anxious or ashamed of aspects of yourself, do you keep someone interested in you or do you tend to become aloof in order to protect yourself from exposure? Try not to run from the truth.

(e) Wait a few days and then think back on the task above.

- How did you approach the task? For example, with reluctance or interest, or did you dismiss it as something silly?

- What was it like thinking about yourself in this way?

- Did you think about it again once you had completed the task?

- What has happened to your resistance – is it greater or lessening?

Notes to Myself

Section 10 – One Breath at a Time

> One day at a time
> One moment at a time
> One breath at a time

'One day at a time' is a phrase frequently used to help those along the road of recovery. Mindfulness takes it even further by emphasising dealing with life one breath at a time, and one moment at a time. Softening the clutches of attachment to anything is difficult and it is a life-long process that can only advance step by step, moment by moment.

Attachments

Attachment is both a wonderful and a strangling experience. At its best, it provides a sense of security, connection and belonging. At its worst, it involves a tie, a bonding that can be stifling and oppressive, even destructive. We are not only attached to people but also to items, values and organisations. Positive and healthy attachments, in psychological terms, are necessary and important in a person's development. However, over-attachment that precludes choice and the freedom for individual thought and experience to occur, is restrictive and repressive.

This can be seen in various aspects of life: whether it be a child (of any age) to a parent, one partner to another, a person to a religion, a desire to accumulate wealth regardless of the consequences, the belief that one is defective in some way, the pursuit of happiness, the maintenance of a social status, and many more.

In one way, to have no attachments must be emancipating as the events of life can come and go without the sorrow of loss. However, to free oneself from any form of attachment is extremely difficult and almost counter-intuitive, as people inherently strive to connect, albeit in different formations (parent to child, lover to lover, friend to friend, sibling to sibling).

There is no right or wrong belief regarding attachments, and whether or not they should be encouraged or discouraged, apart from the need for children to have trusting and secure attachments. As an adult, one can decide if and how one wishes to have and keep the bonds made through life. It is about knowing that there is a space between oneself and the other, whether that be an object (wealth, a job, a house) or a person.

Mindfulness and attachments

Mindfulness, within this context, encourages a review of the attachments you have to your belief system, and the thoughts and actions that emerge from it. We are often so fixed and determined that the situation of now is what will always exist and that our feelings are cast in stone. Just as life can be flexible and transient, so can our beliefs and attachments.

Putting self-criticism, hurt or anger to one side is difficult but not impossible. It's not about denying them or squashing them down but more about noting the impact they have on your life.

We don't have to keep believing something simply because we always have, or because we do so now. This can apply to anything – one's belief about one's body, lovability, appeal, relationships, money, political affiliations, literary likes, and so forth. We tend to think that because we held firmly to one idea at one point that that stand is now immovable.

Exposure to life, with its myriad of experiences and ideas, contributes to our awareness and, therefore, to the choices that we are able to make.

Relinquishing fear

Nothing stays the same, but it is frequently because of fear that we hold on to the old as the new is unfamiliar. If somehow one can be open to an awareness of the new, no matter how small, then there is the chance to take a closer look at it as an observer, and decide whether or not to venture towards it.

The new is often thrust upon us with no time to deliberate, as in a sudden death, an accident, or a diagnosis. Our lives can also change in an instant by meeting a specific person, falling in love, reading a book or watching a programme on television.

We are moved in countless ways, but the impact of the experience can only be known if we give it enough attention. It is then that we can consider how we wish to go about dealing with it, whether it is our grief or our joy.

> Life is about one unknown moment becoming a familiar moment, which is then followed by the next unknown moment.

Waiting to exhale

To attempt to control the future in a frantic and anxious manner disallows us the freedom to be within the present instance of now. Anxiety is often about what we anticipate might happen, and depression is frequently about what has already happened. The problem is we can't actually do anything about either. We hold our breaths in waiting and in expectation. Being aware of our breathing can help keep our physical equilibrium, which will assist towards keeping our emotional balance.

> Humans are strange creatures for their complexities and variances are uncountable, and life is an endless wave that ebbs and flows within and around us.

> Being mindful is as much about enjoying the humour and quirkiness of life and ourselves as it is about recognising the significance of our choices and our approach to life.

Work Choice

(a) Listen to the Mindful Awareness CD (longer or shorter version) whenever you choose.

(b) Consider the attachments in your life:

*   Are they rigid and fixed? Are you anxious and fearful about them as they give you your sense of identity and worth?

*   Do you tend to be guarded and put up barriers for fear of your hidden self being revealed which may lead to rejection or hurt, or do you become over-attached and controlling to try and prevent any possible abandonment or criticism?

*   Do you keep attachments loose and distant in order to avoid worrying about the consequences your behaviour may have on those close to you?

There are many ways in which we can attach to people, animals, possessions or goals,and these may vary according to our situation, age or circumstances.

(d) Identify one specific attachment that has a positive and robust feeling about it, and consider why that is.

(e) Identify an attachment that is unfavourable. Why is it like this, why do you allow it to continue, and what would it be like if you stepped aside from it?

There is no end

You can listen to the Mindful Awareness practice whenever you wish. Some people choose to focus their attention each day, others every second day or once a week. It is worth persisting when listening to the practice even if your mind drifts and jumps around for the first half as it will eventually begin to settle. The fact that you are giving yourself this time, whether it be for two minutes or twenty minutes, is what is important as the process draws you back to an awareness of yourself.

The breathing exercise in Section 2 can be used at any time as a way to refocus yourself. It can be adapted by simply regulating your breathing, either by counting or by concentrating on its flow. Once you begin to settle into the rhythm of your breathing, focus your concentration on the centre of your body for a few moments. When you feel more balanced and in control, then allow your attention to spread back to the everyday noises and activities around you. Imagine going from a wider view, moving towards a central point and then spreading out. Focusing in, stopping, then focusing out. The 5-minute Mindful Awareness practice can also be used.

There are no rules as to how you should do it, or whether you should, and there is no time limit on how long you should meditate or how often.

The more you do it, the easier it is to get into the practice of doing it. More importantly, the more you do it the easier it is to shift your attention to your breathing, and to direct your mind back towards being balanced, dignified and alert.

Once it becomes part of your approach to life, you will be able to bring yourself back to a state of focus and balance within moments simply by reminding yourself to breathe in a mindful manner.

When you pay attention your mindset will shift to your breathing and redirect you to that part that is stable and alive.

Notes to Myself

Section 11 – No Conclusion

The well-worn tracks

My life rattled down the well-worn tracks of life
watching those moments of others' lives
as the train unerringly moved towards its destination.

The man standing, waiting to cross over to a new life
as he watched it pass him by.
The young couple groping playfully
full of the lust and hope of life.

The child
thrilled at the sight and sound of the train
stamped her feet and flung her arms about
in an all-embracing welcome to that moment of her life

reminding me of the newness that still comes
even as I rattle down the well-worn tracks of life.

Life cannot be easily predicted or controlled and people can be filled with dread and terror at the realisation that they are alone. We are not born alone as we are born of another (a mother), and we may or may not die alone, but between those two points a difficult truth to accept is that we are alone to make our choices. This responsibility may, at times, feel like a burden, but it can also bring with it a feeling of power and strength. By taking on this control with energy and enthusiasm, you give yourself the authority and potency to determine the type of mark you wish to leave on this world.

The chances are that you will make mistakes and bad choices, show poor judgements and take ill-chosen decisions along the way, but it's not about how many you can count but about how often you pay attention to them. Mindful decisions can also open the way for you to feel more satisfied with, and excited about, your life. You can savour your life and thrive on the sparkle and humour of an immediate experience rather than have it clouded by anger or lethargy. Feeling lifeless towards life is similar to being awake but in a coma. Mindfulness offers you the chance to bring to life the vitality and power that is present in this moment.

It does not stand alone but is encouraged to be accompanied by kindness and care, humour and delight. In this way it unfolds as an easing up on yourself, an unravelling of some of the tightness and rigidity. It is a means of stepping back and viewing yourself and life with a sense of respect and perspective, for all its harshness and for all its enchantment.

- the sky won't fall on your head if you apologise or admit to a feeling
- there is dignity and pride in being responsible for your choices
- laugh whenever you can

Every drop makes an ocean

In the midst of sheer colour and joy, there is always a speck of darkness, and in the midst of darkness there is always a flicker of light. It is about allowing these aspects to co-exist that creates balance and brings about an awareness that both are there in different measures, at different times, but always together.

We cannot always choose what happens to us

but we can choose how we wish to be within this world.

life happens for better and for worse

that's the way it is

Bibliography

Baer, R. A. (2003). Mindfulness training as a clinical intervention: A conceptual and empirical review. *Clinical Psychology: Science and Practice, 10*(2), 125-143.

Batchelor, S. (1997). *Buddhism without beliefs: A contemporary guide to awakening.* London: Bloomsbury.

Beattie, M. (1987). *Codependent no more: How to stop controlling others and start caring for yourself.* Center City, Minnesota: Hazelden.

Boleyn-Fitzgerald, M. (2010). *Pictures of the mind: What the new neuroscience tells us about who we are.* New Jersey: FT Press.

Bonadonna, R. (2003). Meditation's impact on chronic illness. *Holistic Nursing Practice, 17*(6), 309-19.

Bowlby, J. (1980). *Loss: Sadness and depression. Attachment and loss (Vol. 3).* London: Hogarth Press.

Brantley, J. (2003). *Calming your anxious mind.* Oakland, CA: New Harbinger.

Brewer, J.A., Bowen, S., Smith, J.T., Marlatt, G.A., & Potenza, M.N. (2010). Mindfulness-based treatments for co-occurring depression and substance use disorders: What can we learn from the brain? *Addiction.* Advance online publication. doi:10.1111/j.1360-0443.2009.02890.

Burch, V. (2008). *Living well with pain and illness: The mindful way to free yourself from suffering.* London: Piatkus.

Carlson, L.E., Speca, M., Patel, K.D., & Goodey, E. (2004). Mindfulness-based stress reduction in relation to quality of life, mood, symptoms of stress and levels of cortisol, dehydroepiandrosterone sulphate (DHEAS) and melatonin in breast and prostate cancer outpatients. *Psychoneuroendocrinology, 29*(4), 448-474.

Dakwar, A., & Levin, F. (2009). The emerging role of meditation in addressing psychiatric illness, with a focus on substance use disorders. *Harvard Review of Psychiatry, 17*(4), 254-67.

Davidson, R. J., Kabat-Zinn, J., Schmacher, J., Rosenbranz, B.A., Muller, D., Santorelli, S.F., Urbanowski, F., Harrington, A., Bonus, K., & Sheridan, J.F. (2003). Alterations in brain and immune function produced by mindfulness meditation. *Psychosomatic Medicine, 65*(4), 564-570.

Davis, J.M., Fleming, M.F., Bonus, K.A., & Baker, T.B. (2007). A pilot study on mindfulness-based stress reduction for smokers. *BMC Complementary Alternative Medicine, 25*(7), 2.

De Zulueta, F. (1993). *From pain to violence: The traumatic roots of destructiveness.* London: Whurr.

Edelman, D., Oddone, E.Z., Liebowitz, R.S., Yancy, W.S., Oslen, M.K., Jeffreys, A.S., Moon, S.D., Harris, A.C., Smith, L.L., Quillian-Wolever, R.E., & Gaudet, T.W. (2006). A multidimensional integrative medicine intervention to improve cardiovascular risk. *Journal of General Internal Medicine, 21*(7), 728-734.

Erikson, E. (1963). *Childhood and society (2nd ed.).* New York: Norton.

Erikson, E. (1968). *Identity: Youth and crisis.* New York: Norton.

Farb, N., Segal, Z., Mayberg, H., Bean, J., McKeon, D., Fatima, Z., & Anderson, A. (2007). Attending to the present: Mindfulness meditation reveals distinct neural modes of self-reference. *Social, Cognitive and Affective Neuroscience, 2*, 313-322.

Gardner-Nix, J. (2009). *The mindfulness solution to pain.* Oakland, CA: New Harbinger.

Greeson, J.M. (2009). Mindfulness research update: 2008. *Complementary Health Practice Reviews, 14*(1), 10-18.

Grossman, P., Niemann, M.A., Schmidt, S. & Walach, H. (2004). Mindfulness-based stress reduction and health benefits: A meta-analysis. *Journal of Psychosomatic Research, 57*(1), 35-43.

Gunaratana, B. H. (2002). *Mindfulness in plain English.* Boston: Wisdom.

Jacobs-Stewart, T. (2010). *Mindfulness and the 12 steps: Living recovery in the present moment.* Center City, Minnesota: Hazelden.

Kabat-Zinn, J. (2003). Mindfulness-based interventions in context: Past, present and future. *Clinical Psychology Science and Practice, 10*, 144-156.

Kabat-Zinn, J. (2005). *Coming to our senses: Healing ourselves and the world through mindfulness.* New York: Hyperion.

Kabat-Zin, J., Lipworth, L., Burney, R., & Sellers, W. (1986). Four-year follow-up of a meditation-based program for self-regulation of chronic pain: Treatment outcomes and compliance. *Clinical Journal of Pain, 2,* 159-173.

Kabat-Zinn, J., Wheeler, E., Light, T, Skillings, A., Scharf, M.S., Cropley, T.G., Hosmer, D., & Bernhard, J.D. (1986). Influence of a mindfulness-based stress reduction intervention on rates of skin clearing in patients with moderate to severe psoriasis undergoing phototherapy (UVB) and photochemotherapy (PUVA). *Psychotherapy and Psychosomatic Medicine, 60,* 625-631.

Kaplan, K.H., Goldenberg, D.L., & Galvin-Nadeau, M. (1993). The impact of a meditation-based stress reduction program on fibromyalgia. *General Hospital Psychiatry, 15,* 284-289.

Kieviet-Stjinen, A., Visser, A., Garssen, B., & Hudig, W. (2008). Mindfulness-based stress reduction training for oncology patients: Patients' appraisal and changes in well-being. *Patient Education and Counseling, 72*(3), 436-342.

Kornfield, J. (1994). *A path with heart.* New York: Bantam.

Kristeller, J.L., & Hallett, C.B. (1999). An exploratory study of a meditation-based intervention for binge-eating disorder. *Journal of Health Psychology, 4,* 357-363.

LeDoux, J. (1996). *The emotional brain.* New York: Touchstone.

Mansky, P., & Wallerstedt, D.B. (2006). Complementary medicine in palliative care and cancer symptom management. *Cancer Journal, 12*(5), 425-431.

Mills, N., & Allen, J. (2000). Mindfulness of movement as a coping strategy in multiple sclerosis: A pilot study. *General Hospital Psychiatry, 22,* 425-431.

Moore, A., & Malinowski, P. (2009). Meditation, mindfulness and cognitive flexibility. *Conscious Cognition, 18*(1), 176-186.

Morone, N.E., Greco, C.M., & Weiner, D.K. (2008). Mindfulness meditation for the treatment of chronic low back pain in older adults: A randomized controlled pilot study. *Pain, 134*(3), 310-319.

Morone, N.E., Lynch, C.S., Greco, C.M., Tindle, H.A., & Weiner, D.K. (2008). 'I felt like a new person'. The effects of mindfulness meditation on older adults with chronic pain: Qualitative narrative analysis of diary entries. *Journal of Pain, 9*(9), 841-848.

Ott, M.J., Norris, R.L., & Bauer-Wu, S.M. (2006). Mindfulness meditation for oncology patients: A discussion and critical review. *Integrative Cancer Therapies, 5*(2), 98-108.

Palesh, O., Zeitzer, J.M., Conrad, A., Giese-Davis, J., Mustian, K., Popek, V., Nga, K., & Spiegel, D. (2008). Vagal regulation, cortisol, and sleep disruption in women with metastatic breast cancer. *Journal of Clinical Sleep Medicine, 4*(5), 441-449.

Perry, B.D. (1999). Memories of fear: How the brain stores and retrieves physiological states, feelings, behaviors and thoughts from traumatic events. In J. Goodwin & R. Attial (Eds.), *Splintered reflections: Images of the body in trauma*. New York: Basic Books.

Perry, B.D., Pollard, R.A., Baker, W.L., Sturges, C., Vigilanted, D., & Blakely, T.L. (1995). Childhood trauma, the neurobiology of adaptation and 'use-dependent' development of the brain: How 'states' become 'traits'. *Infant Mental Health Journal, 16*(4), 271-291.

Phillips, A. (1988). *Winnicott*. London: Fontana Press.

Pradhan, E., Baumgarten, M., Langenberg, P., Hanwerger, B., Kaplan Gilpin, A., Magyari, M., Hochberg, M., & Berman, B. (2007). Effect of mindfulness-based stress reduction in rheumatoid arthritis patients. *Arthritis and Rheumatism, 57*(7), 1134-1142.

Pruett, JM., Nishimura, N.J., & Priest, R. (2007). The role of meditation in addiction recovery. *Counseling and Values, 52*(1), 71-85.

Randolph, P.D., Caldera, Y.M., Tacone, A.M., & Greak, M.I. (1999). The long-term combined effects of medical treatment and a mindfulness-based behavioral program for the multidisciplinary management of chronic pain in West Texas. *Pain Digest, 9*, 103-112.

Reinherz, H.Z., Giaconia, R.M., Pakiz, B., Silverman, A.B., Frost, A.K., & Lefkowitz, E.S. (1993). Psychosocial risks for major depression in late adolescence: A longitudinal community study. *Journal of the American Academy of Child and Adolescent Psychiatry, 32*, 1155-1163.

Rezek, C.A. (2003). The avoidance of traumatic memories in depressed, recovering depressed and never depressed individuals. In C.A. Rezek, *Depression across early, middle and late adulthood* (pp. 41-184). (Doctoral dissertation, City University London/ British Library). Retrieved May, 2010, from http://www.cherylrezek.com/articles.

Rezek, C.A. (2003). Depression in older adults – is it worthy of treatment and recognition? In C.A. Rezek, *Depression across early, middle and late adulthood* (pp. 185-230). (Doctoral dissertation, City University London/British Library). Retrieved May, 2010, from http://www.cherylrezek.com/articles.

Rezek, C.A. (2007). The heart of therapy. *Clinical Psychology Forum*, 179, 38-40.

Rezek, C.A. (2009). *Development and implementation of a forensic addictions programme in a secure setting*. Retrieved May, 2010, from http://www.cherylrezek.com/articles.

Ricard, M. (2010). *The art of meditation*. London: Atlantic Books.

Robert-McComb, J., Tacone, A., Randolph, P., & Caldera, Y. (2004). A pilot study to examine the effects of a mindfulness-based stress-reduction and relaxation program on levels of stress hormones, physical functioning, and submaximal exercise responses. *Journal of Alternative and Complementary Medicine, 10*(5), 819-827.

Rosenbaum, E. (2005). *Here for now: Living well with cancer through mindfulness*. Hardwick, Massachusetts: Satya House.

Rosenzweig, S., Reibel, Dk., Greeson, J.M., Edman, J.S., Jasser, S.A., McMearty, K.D., & Goldstein, B.J. (2007). Mindfulness-based stress reduction is associated with improved glycemic control in Type 2 diabetes mellitus: A pilot study. *Alternative Therapies, 13*(5), 36-38.

Roth, B. (1997). Mindfulness-based stress reduction in the inner city. *Advances, 13*, 50-58.

Rothschild, B. (2000). *The body remembers: The psychophysiology of trauma and trauma treatment*. New York: Norton & Co.

Rubin, T.I. (1975). *Compassion and self-hate: An alternative to despair*. New York: Ballantyne Books.

Santorelli, S. (1999). *Heal thyself: Lessons on mindfulness in medicine*. New York: Bell Tower.

Schofferman, J., Anderson, D., Hines, R., Smith, G., & Keane, G. (1993). Childhood psychological trauma and chronic refractory low-back pain. *Clinical Journal of Pain, 4*, 260-265.

Sephton, S.E., Salmon, P., Weissbecker, I., Ulmer, C., Floyd, A., Hoover, K., & Studts, J.L. (2007). Mindfulness meditation alleviates depressive symptoms in women with fibromyalgia: Results of a randomized clinical trial. *Arthritis and Rheumatism, 15*, 57(1), 77-85.

Shah, R., & Waller, G. (2000). Parental style and vulnerability to depression. *Journal of Nervous and Mental Disease, 188*(1), 19-25.

Siegel, D.J. (2007). Mindfulness training and neural integration: Differentiation of distinct streams of awareness and the cultivation of well-being. *Social, Cognitive and Affective Neuroscience, 2*(4), 250-263.

Speca, M., Carlson, L.E., Goodey, E., & Angen, M. (2000). A randomized, wait-list controlled clinical trial: the effect of a mindfulness-based stress reduction program on mood and symptoms of stress in cancer outpatients. *Psychosomatic Medicine, 62*, 613- 622.

Storr, A. (1968). *Human aggression.* Middlesex: Penguin.

Storr, A. (1989). *Freud.* Oxford: Oxford University Press.

Storr, A. (1989). *Solitude.* London: Flamingo.

Sullivan, M.J., Wood, L., Terry, J., Brantley, J., Charles, A., McGee, V., Johnson, D., Krucoff, M.W., Rosenberg, B., Bosworth, H.B., Adams, K., & Cuffe, M.S. (2009). The support, education, and research in chronic heart failure study (SEARCH): A mindfulness-based psychoeducational intervention improves depression and clinical symptoms in patients with chronic heart failure. *American Heart Journal, 157*(1), 84-90.

Surawy, C., Roberts, J., & Silver, S. (2005). The effect of mindfulness training on mood and measures of fatigue, activity and quality of life in patients with chronic fatigue syndrome on a hospital waiting list: A series of exploratory studies. *Behavioral and Cognitive Psychotherapy, 33*, 103-109.

Thich Nhat Hanh. (1991). *The miracle of mindfulness.* London: Rider.

Twerski, A.J. (1990). *Addictive thinking: Why we lie to ourselves? Why do others believe us?* Center City, Minnesota: Hazelden.

van der Kolk, B.A., McFarlane, A.C., & Weisaeth, L (Eds.). (1996). *Traumatic stress: The effects of overwhelming experience on mind, body, and society.* New York: Guilford Press.

Vestergaard-Poulsen, P., van Beek, M., Skewes, J., Bjarkam, C.R., Stubberup, M., Bertelsen, J., & Roepstorff. A. (2009). Long-term meditation is associated with increased gray matter density in the brain stem. *Neuroreport, 20*(2), 170-174.

Wegscheider-Cruise, S., & Cruise, J. (1990). *Understanding codependency.* Deerfield Beach, Florida: Health Communications, Inc.

Welberg, L.A.M., & Seckl, J.R. (2001). Prenatal stress, glucocorticoids and the programming of the brain. *Journal of Neuroendocrinology, 13,* 113-128.

Winnicott, D.W. (1964). *The child, the family, and the outside world.* Middlesex: Penguin.

Yehuda, R., Resnick, H., Kahana, B., & Giller, E.L. (1986). Long-lasting hormonal alterations to extreme stress in humans: Normative or maladaptive? *Psychosomatic Medicine, 55,* 287-297.

Zeidan, F., Gordon, N.S., Merchant, J., & Goolkasian, P. (2010). The effects of brief mindfulness meditation training on experimentally induced pain. *The Journal of Pain, 11*(3), 199-209.

Zylowska, L., Ackerman, D.L., Yang, M.H., Futrell, J.L., Horton, N.L., Hale, T.S., Pataki, C., & Smalley, S.L. (2008). Mindfulness meditation training in adults and adolescents with ADHD: A feasibility study. *Journal of Attention Disorders, 11*(6), 737-746.

Some useful websites:

www.addictionrecoveryguide.org.

www.arthritistoday.org
(www.arthritistoday/symptoms/pain/meditation-and-pain-management.php).

www.bangor.ac.uk/mindfulness. Centre for Mindfulness Research and Practice, School of Psychology, Bangor University, Bangor, Wales, UK.

www.childdevelopmentinfo.com

www.childtrauma.org

www.clarityseminars/stress_clinical_research.html (clinical research on stress, meditation and health, including the effects of stress on health and productivity, and clinical research on the benefits of meditation, including heart disease, insomnia, chronic pain, mental health, addiction and so forth).

www.fibromyalgia-symptoms.org/fibromyalgia-meditation.html.

www.learning-theories.com/eriksons-stages-of-development.html

www.mindandlife.org (material on neuroscience and meditation, neuroplasticity and so forth).

www.mindfulnet.org (this site provides extensive material on research into mindfulness, its applications, the different branches that are developing and many other topics).

www.patientvoices.org.uk. This is a digital storytelling site where patients, carers and professionals are provided the opportunity to tell, hear and share personal stories of their experiences involving healthcare issues, such as living with a chronic illness, losing a child, or being a manager of services.

www.scholastic.com/bruceperry (articles on child development, the brain and learning, children in distress and others).

www.umassmed.edu/cfm. Centre for Mindfulness, University of Massachusetts Worcester Campus, North Worcester, Massachusetts, USA. The original Mindfulness–Based Stress Reduction (MBSR) programme was developed, implemented and researched here.